D0359671

Series 561

A Ladybird History Book

INDEX

Book 2

Kings and Queens

by L. DU GARDE PEACH
M.A., Ph.D., D.Litt.

with illustrations by
FRANK HAMPSON

Publishers: Wills & Hepworth Ltd., Loughborough
First published 1968 © *Printed in England*

Henry VII 1485-1509

The claim of King Henry VII to the throne was a weak one, though it was strengthened by his victory at Bosworth, on the battlefield of which he was immediately crowned. His mother was descended from John of Gaunt, Duke of Lancaster, but he decided to make his claim even better by marrying Elizabeth of York, sister of the murdered boy king, Edward V.

Henry VII was a wise king. He realised that in the past the country had suffered because it was poor. Taxes had often been too high, and the money so gained had been wasted. He determined to put an end to expensive wars abroad, and to make taxation fair at home.

This was the century when men began to know more about the far countries of the earth. A Portuguese prince, known as Henry the Navigator, had sent ships to Africa and the Azores. More important, he had founded a school of navigation.

John Cabot, an Italian sailor, had settled in England, and Henry VII ordered him to 'seek out unknown lands'. He sailed away in 1496 and discovered North America, four years after Columbus. Henry VII generously awarded him an annual pension of £20!

Henry VII is crowned on Bosworth Field.

7214 0183 X

Henry VIII 1509-1547

Henry VIII was the right kind of king needed by England at the beginning of the XVI century. He was strong and ruthless, but he was also clever and determined that England should be powerful and prosperous.

The fact that he was married six times is what is usually remembered about him. This is only important because his second marriage was the reason for the establishment of the Church of England. Henry's great Chancellor was Cardinal Wolsey, who lived in greater state than the King himself. Henry's other claim to remembrance is that he reconstituted the Navy, for which he caused to be built the largest ship then afloat, the beautiful ship 'Henry, Grace à Dieu'.

In the Tudor period, beginning with Henry VII, houses of a new kind were built in England. Many of them can be recognised today by their square-topped windows, divided by upright stone divisions called mullions.

Inside, they had decorated fireplaces leading to elaborate chimneys on the roof. Red brick was often used, and Hampton Court, built by Cardinal Wolsey, and St. James's Palace are fine examples. Rooms were beautifully panelled in oak, and houses became so much more comfortable that many Tudor houses are still occupied today.

Henry VIII proudly reviews his new fleet from the poop of the 'Henry, Grace à Dieu'

Edward VI 1547-1553

Edward VI was only nine years old when he became king, and the country was governed by two men: first by the King's uncle, the Duke of Somerset, and later by the Earl of Warwick. Although only fifteen when he died, Edward had already shown signs that he might have been a good ruler.

The event most connected with Edward VI's short reign was the issue of the Church of England Prayer Book in English. At the same time the taking over of the lands and treasures of the monasteries continued. This had been started by Henry VIII, and many people became very rich on the land which they were given by the King.

Ever since Anglo-Saxon times the monasteries had become more and more wealthy and powerful. For hundreds of years they had been the only centres of learning. They had ministered to the sick and provided shelter for travellers at a time when no-one else did either.

Through the years, many people left rich gifts of treasure or land to the monasteries, and the monks grew fat and lazy. The abbots lived like rich country gentlemen, and the real usefulness of the monasteries to the country no longer remained.

The Lord Protectors arguing in front of the boy king at a Council of State.

Mary 1553-1558

Queen Mary reigned for five years. If she had reigned longer, it might have been disastrous for England. She hated her father, Henry VIII, for having divorced her mother, and she hated the Church of England, which Henry had established to make the divorce possible.

Mary was a Catholic, and the year after she came to the throne she married the Catholic king of Spain, Philip II. Her one aim in life was to make England a Catholic country again, and she was ready to agree to anything to bring this about.

There had been religious persecution in England before, but under Queen Mary it grew very much worse. Many hundreds of those who refused to become Catholics were put to death or savagely tortured. The effect of this was to make Mary hated by the greater part of the population of England.

Mary had caused England to make war on France in support of her husband, Philip of Spain. The only result of the war was the loss of Calais, which England had held ever since the time of William the Conqueror. When Mary died she said that 'Calais' would be found engraved on her heart.

The arrest of a Protestant preacher.

Elizabeth I 1558-1603

When Mary died and her younger sister Elizabeth became Queen, the people felt safe again. So did Elizabeth. Mary had become insanely jealous of her, but Elizabeth, at twenty-five, was one of the cleverest women in the country, and although she was a Protestant, she managed to stay alive even though many others were executed.

We always remember two events when we think of Elizabeth: the great victory at sea over the mighty Spanish Armada, and the execution of Mary, Queen of Scots. Each of them shows us something of the character of Elizabeth: her magnificent courage when she went to Tilbury to encourage her soldiers under the threat of invasion, and her determination to put an end to Mary's claim to the English throne, and all the plots and conspiracies which resulted from it.

It was in Elizabeth's reign that sailors like Raleigh and Drake, Hawkins, Frobisher, and many others, sailed what was called the Spanish Main, intercepting and capturing the Spanish treasure ships and discovering new lands. Virginia, in America, is still named after Elizabeth.

In London, regular theatres were built and plays were produced, including those of the greatest writer of all time, William Shakespeare. In these plays, all the women's parts were played by young men.

12

The night of July 28th, 1588. English fire-ships driving on the anchored Armada in Calais roads.

Elizabeth I (continued)

Queen Elizabeth never married. Many of the kings and princes of Europe were willing to become the Prince Consort of the Queen of England, but Elizabeth knew that so long as they were hoping to marry the Queen, they would remain friendly to her country. She very cleverly played one off against the other.

In forming a picture of Elizabeth's time, we must remember that although it was the age of Shakespeare, of poetry, art and music and of much great architecture, there were many things which we should miss, and many which we should dislike.

There were no bathrooms in the beautiful mansions built by the enormously rich noblemen, and nobody washed very much. Even Elizabeth is said to have taken a bath only once a month. The streets of the towns were filthy, and often had open drains running down the middle of them. The houses of ordinary people were built of wood, were highly inflammable and infested with rats.

However, the sailors of England were magnificent. Englishmen were proud of their Queen and of their country, a pride which shines through the poems and plays of Shakespeare. He called England, 'This jewel set in a silver sea!'

Queen Elizabeth I prepares to take a bath.

James I 1603-1625

When Elizabeth died, James VI of Scotland was the next heir to the throne. He was descended from a daughter of Henry VII who had married the Scottish King James IV. So James VI of Scotland became James I of England.

James was never a popular king. He was ungainly and slovenly in appearance, and untrustworthy and deceitful. He believed that a king could do no wrong, and his persecution of the Catholics resulted in many plots being formed against him.

The best known is the Gunpowder Plot. It is today associated with Guy Fawkes, although many others were also involved in it. If it had succeeded, James and both Houses of Parliament would have been blown up. It was discovered because one of the conspirators warned a relation to stay away from the opening of Parliament on November 5th, 1605.

It was by order of James that the Authorised Edition of the Bible was made, and every copy today has printed in it a dedication to him. This is to his credit, but his oppression of the Puritans caused a number of them to sail in the 'Mayflower' in 1620 and to found New England in North America.

The 'Mayflower' sails to America.

Charles I 1625-1649

Like his father, James I, King Charles believed in the Divine Right of Kings, that is the belief that a king can do no wrong. He was not a stupid man, but he was obstinate and deceitful. He did not realise that the people of England were determined to rule the country by means of their freely elected Parliament. When they found that the King's word was never to be trusted, a bitter struggle was certain.

James I had been very extravagant and had left the country very poor. Charles had to raise money somehow, and he tried to make people pay all sorts of illegal taxes. He quarrelled with Parliament and on one occasion went himself to Parliament with a number of soldiers to arrest five of the Members. But they had been warned of his intentions and had gone into hiding. On his way back through London the King was openly jeered at by the citizens.

This was a time when the clothes of fashionable men became very elaborate. They wore long hair, and their shirts and doublets were decorated with lace and ribbons.

Charles I reviews his Royalist Volunteers at the beginning of the Civil War.

Cromwell 1653-1658

When he found himself defied by Parliament, King Charles decided to rule the country by force. He left London and called all men who were on his side to assemble at Nottingham. Here he gathered an army.

Parliament raised an army to meet him, and the long years of the Civil War followed. There is no space here to tell the grim story of battles and sieges, when Englishmen fought and killed Englishmen. Finally the King, treacherous and deceitful to the last, was captured and executed.

England became a Commonwealth, and the man who had proved himself an able general in the Civil War became its ruler. He was a gentleman-farmer from Huntingdon, Oliver Cromwell, and his title was Lord Protector.

Cromwell was stern but tolerant. He ruled England well, and made her army and navy the best in the world. But, like King Charles, he had trouble with Parliament. It is recorded that finally he drove the Members out, locked the door, and put the key in his pocket. During this period the people of England had few pleasures. Dancing was considered wicked, and there were no theatres. Many people dressed in drab clothes and life must have been very dull.

Cromwell addresses the Parliamentary troops.

Charles II 1660-1685

When Cromwell died there was no-one to succeed him. The country was tired of being ruled by men who hated pleasure in any form, and in 1660 the son of Charles I returned to England from exile and became Charles II.

He was the exact opposite to Cromwell and the Puritans. He was witty, amusing and popular. He was also one of the cleverest kings ever to occupy the English throne. He enjoyed music and dancing, and encouraged the new theatres in which, for the first time, women appeared on the stage.

England was merry again under Charles II, but within five years there came the terrible Plague of London, in which at least a hundred thousand people died. Narrow and dirty streets, open drains, and old rat-infested houses, all helped the plague to spread.

Scarcely had the plague died away than two thirds of the houses in London were destroyed in the Great Fire. In the end this proved a good thing because when new houses were built, they were of stone, not of wood, and streets were wider if not much cleaner.

Charles II directs troops fighting the Great Fire of London.

James II 1685-1689

James II, the younger brother of Charles, was brave and intelligent, but he was a Catholic, and his two aims were to make England a Catholic country, and himself an absolute monarch. He failed in both.

He was so unpopular with Parliament and the people that when the Protestant William of Orange landed at Torbay to claim the crown, many thousands of men, including a large part of the army, joined him. James fled in disguise, dropping the Great Seal of England into the Thames as he did so. He hoped, in vain, by this stupid action to make the government of England impossible.

The long coastline of England, and perhaps also the Viking blood of its mixed people, have made Englishmen daring sailors. Alfred had sent ships out on voyages of discovery, and Henry VII had sent John Cabot to explore the frozen north of Canada.

During Elizabeth's reign, Raleigh and others had started small colonies in America, and during the time of James I the Pilgrim Fathers had sailed to New England. Under Charles II an English fleet captured New Amsterdam in America and re-named it New York. Today it has become one of the most famous cities in the world.

William and Mary (d. 1694) 1689-1702

William of Orange and his wife Mary were cousins, and both were descended from Charles I. They reigned together because each had a claim to the throne. When Mary died in 1694 William remained on the throne as William III.

William was a foreigner in England, and his fondness for his native country, Holland, made him unpopular. But the fact that both he and Mary were Protestants was a relief to the nation after the Catholic James II. All people were free to worship as they pleased.

It was during the reign of William and Mary that the Bank of England was founded by a Scot named Paterson. There had been banks before, both in England and elsewhere. The earliest known was in Babylon, four thousand years ago. The ancient Egyptians, the Greeks, and the Romans also had banks.

In mediaeval England it was dangerous for people to keep money in their houses, or to carry it from place to place. Therefore they often left it with some honest merchant who gave them a receipt. Then a merchant in some other town would give them the money which the receipt represented. This was the beginning of banking in England.

A wealthy merchant being robbed on the highway.

Anne 1702-1714

Anne was the younger sister of Mary, and when William died she came to the throne, the first woman to reign since Elizabeth.

Queen Anne was a good woman, popular with her subjects, but unfortunately she was not very clever. This meant, however, that Parliament became more important than ever, and since her reign its power has never been questioned.

Her reign is always associated with the great general, the Duke of Marlborough, an ancestor of Sir Winston Churchill. In the war with France he won the great victories of Blenheim and Malplaquet. His wife, Sarah, Duchess of Marlborough, was for a long time a close friend of Queen Anne, and had a great influence over her. The wonderful palace of Blenheim was built by Queen Anne as a tribute from the people of England to the Duke.

Both in buildings and in furniture we recognise a change in design which began in Queen Anne's time. With the coming of William of Orange, Dutch type houses built of red brick, with flat fronts and evenly spaced windows, were built in England. Many of these are still to be found in London and in small market towns up and down England.

Anne signs the Act of Union with Scotland.

George I 1714-1727

The next heir to the throne of England was George, the Elector of Hanover. He was the ruler of a small German state, but his grandmother had been a daughter of James I.

George I was fifty-four years of age when he became King of England. He was a very stupid man, and as he never took the trouble to learn to speak English, he was unpopular with everybody. As a king he was completely unimportant.

It was during his reign that England first had a Prime Minister. There had always been men who advised the King, but they had been the King's friends or great noblemen. Now the Chief Minister of the Crown was chosen by Parliament, and the King was bound to act on his advice. This system of government is known as a Constitutional Monarchy, and it has continued to the present day.

Today everybody reads newspapers, and there have been newspapers of a sort ever since the days of Charles I. It was during the time of the four Georges that newspapers became common. Daniel Defoe who was born in 1659, was the first English journalist of any importance. His paper, 'The Review', appeared three times a week.

Some of the first newspapers being delivered by coach.

George II 1727-1760

It was said of George II that his greatest pleasure was counting his money, piece by piece. He was just and honest, but not very intelligent. This was to the benefit of the country, because during his reign the King had less and less influence in the Government.

In 1745 there occurred the last invasion of England by the Scots, and King George was so frightened that he had his bags packed, ready to hurry away to Hanover. The invasion, known always as the '45, was by Prince Charles, the grandson of James II, who had actually a better claim to the throne than George.

The invasion failed. Prince Charles and his men got as far as Derby, but on his way back to the Highlands he was beaten at the battle of Culloden, and his cause was lost for ever.

It was during this period that some of the most beautiful of English furniture was made by such men as Chippendale and Hepplewhite, and later by Sheraton. Pieces of furniture made by them are today very valuable. Many of the handsome London squares were also built in the Georgian period, and museums and private collections contain fine silver articles made by Georgian craftsmen.

Prince Charles' Highland Army marches south through England.

George III 1760-1820

George III was the victim of an inherited disease from which his far-off ancestor James I had also suffered. This made life very difficult for him, and sometimes he seemed to become quite insane. Like Charles I, he wanted to make himself the absolute ruler of the country, but only succeeded in strengthening the power of Parliament.

With the help of his chief minister, Lord North, he lost the American colonies by trying to make them pay taxes without their consent. The last straw was when he put a tax on tea. In the war which followed, the Americans, led by George Washington, won and became a free people. George Washington was their first President.

In France a revolution broke out, and the king, Louis XVI, was executed. The countries of Europe combined against France, but under Napoleon, the greatest general of all time, France was everywhere victorious. Britain alone remained unconquered. Finally, Napoleon was beaten at sea by Nelson at Trafalgar, and on land by Wellington at Waterloo.

The long wars had left England very poor, and a tax on personal incomes was instituted to pay for them. At first it was only a few pence in the pound: today it is many shillings.

Resentful Americans watch the occupation of their town by British and Hessian troops of George III.

George IV 1820-1830

George IV was even more unpopular than his father. When he drove through the streets, stones were thrown at his carriage, and he had to be protected by soldiers. He was selfish and vain, and evidence of his stupid extravagance may still be seen in the Pavilion which he built at Brighton.

England was changing under the Georges. Steam engines were invented, and factories were built for spinning and weaving. Up to this time such work had been done by workers at home. Now they had to live near the factories, and the towns of England, which had remained much the same as they were under Elizabeth, began to grow larger.

Up to the accession of George IV, all travelling was by horse-drawn coaches or on horseback. This was very slow and uncomfortable. The early carriages were without springs, and the roads were very bad. A journey from Glasgow to London took more than a week.

It was not until the reign of George III that two Scots, Telford and MacAdam, built good roads, but travelling was still by coach until the first railway was built by Stephenson in 1825. The early trains, in which passengers travelled in open trucks, were as uncomfortable as the coaches had been.

An early type of train with open passenger trucks.

William IV 1830-1837

William IV, younger brother of George IV, had been a sailor, and his chief interest was the Navy. He was a timid, cautious man who often made himself ridiculous by very foolish speeches. As a king he was a failure.

We have seen how King John was forced to grant reforms under Magna Carta, and how a Parliament was summoned by Simon de Montfort under Henry III. During the following reigns, King and Parliament were often quarrelling, until Parliament became supreme with the coming of William of Orange.

Up to the time of William IV the Members of Parliament were not elected by the people as a whole. Many of them were chosen by some nobleman because he owned a lot of land, others by bribing the electors. In 1832 a law was passed giving the vote to everyone paying ten pounds a year rent.

Ever since the time of Elizabeth, negroes had been seized in Africa and sold as slaves to work on the plantations in the new colonies in America. It is very regrettable that many Englishmen should have grown rich by this means. However, in the year 1833, slavery was finally abolished by law.

Ashanti slaves being embarked from the Gold Coast on American slave-ships.

Victoria 1837-1901

Queen Victoria, the niece of William IV, reigned through a period of tremendous changes in Britain and in the world. She was obstinate and not very clever, but she was sincere and devoted to her country.

During her reign, England became the centre of the greatest Empire the world has ever known. By the time she died, Victoria ruled over one quarter of the globe. She became Empress of India, the conquest of which had been begun by Clive in the reign of George II.

When Victoria came to the throne, people were still travelling in stage coaches, and wooden sailing ships carried the cargoes of the world. A paddle steamer of seven hundred tons was considered a big ship in 1838. By 1900, railways covered the country, the great ship *Mauritania* was soon to be built, and men were already experimenting with aeroplanes and gliders.

The telegraph and telephone had been invented, and Marconi had sent a message from England to America by wireless. The phonograph and the kinetoscope, respectively the beginnings of the gramophone and the moving pictures, had been invented by Edison in America. Medicine had made tremendous advances, and proper drainage and pure water supplies made people more healthy.

Queen Victoria taking a rail journey with Albert and family about 1850.

Edward VII 1901-1910

Edward was sixty when his mother died and he became King. He had never been allowed by Victoria to have any part in affairs of state, and his main interests were sport and travel. He knew every important man and every ruling monarch in Europe, and was quite at home in many continental capitals.

Edward has been called the Peacemaker, and he did a great deal to bring about real friendship between England and France. This was to be severely tested within a few years of his death. Edward's common sense, and his habit of mixing freely with the people, made him a popular king.

The first ten years of the 20th century were socially gay. England was wealthy and at peace. London was the centre of the world, and English goods were sought after everywhere. Riches poured into the country from the vast Empire.

One event, perhaps more than any other, gave a hint of what was to come. On July 25th, 1909, a Frenchman named Bleriot flew across the English Channel in a very simple and primitive aeroplane. This meant that England could no longer be protected by the ships which, age after age, had been built for her defence.

Louis· Bleriot flies the Channel.

George V 1910-1936

George V had not expected to become King, and had been trained as a naval officer. When his elder brother died, he became heir to the throne and King in 1910. George V was a very conscientious man and a good and popular king.

The First World War broke out four years later. Germany was beaten, but a great many things happened as a result.

The Russians rose against their ruler, the Czar Nicholas II, and became a communist country. Before the end of the reign of George V there were revolutions in two other countries, Germany and Italy, and two evil men, Hitler and Mussolini, became dictators. They were later responsible for the outbreak of the Second World War.

In England great changes took place. New Acts of Parliament gave women the right to vote, and the number of voters increased from seven millions to twenty millions. Trade was bad, and three years after the end of the war there were two million people in England without work. During the early part of the reign of George V, pensions were granted to widows and old people by a government under a Welshman named Lloyd George. He also helped to found the League of Nations, in an attempt to secure world peace.

George V, accompanied by the Prince of Wales, talks to a French officer on the Western Front.

Edward VIII (Duke of Windsor) 1936

When King George V died, his eldest son became King as Edward VIII. He was never crowned. When he announced his intention to marry a divorced woman, Parliament told him that if he did so, he would have to abdicate – that is, cease to be King. So Edward VIII became the Duke of Windsor, and was succeeded by his younger brother.

When we look back over the history of Parliament in England, we realise how it has grown in power. It was able, without a Civil War such as had led to the execution of Charles I, quietly to depose the rightful King of England.

As Prince of Wales, Edward had been very popular. He had visited many of the dominions and colonies, and had taken a personal interest in the work and the lives of ordinary people. When there was a lot of unemployment amongst the miners of South Wales, he had gone amongst them and tried to help.

This made him popular with the miners, but not with Parliament. The Royal Family is not permitted to interfere in politics. In a democracy, where the people rule, the Civil Service, the Armed Forces, and the Monarch must take no part in politics.

Edward visits the unemployed in Wales.

George VI 1936-1952

When Edward VIII abdicated, George VI became King unexpectedly. Like his father, he had been trained as a naval officer and would have preferred to remain one. But he became a good and popular king.

During his reign, the evil dictator of Germany, Adolph Hitler, broke all the promises which Germany had made after the First World War, and treacherously invaded Poland. Germany had been secretly training an army and air force, and soon Hitler had conquered all western Europe. A British army was forced to retreat, and to return to England from Dunkirk.

For a year Britain, inspired by one of the greatest men in our history, Winston Churchill, fought alone against Hitler's Germany. London and many cities in England were heavily bombed. George VI remained in London, even though Buckingham Palace was partly bombed, and he frequently visited the devastated streets and houses, encouraging and helping those made homeless. Later, Russia became involved in the war against Germany, and also the United States of America came in on our side – and so final victory was certain, though not without great suffering to many millions of people.

Since the war a second attempt has been made to secure peace by founding the United Nations, but this has been only partly successful.

The Battle of Britain, 1940.

Elizabeth II 1952-

George VI died at the age of 57, and his eldest daughter, Elizabeth, became the fourth English queen to reign in her own right. In England she reigns as Elizabeth II, but in Scotland, which never came under the rule of Elizabeth Tudor, she is known as Elizabeth I.

During the years following the Second World War, Britain could be almost proud of her poverty. Her vast wealth had been poured out to preserve freedom in the world. Countries like India, Pakistan, Ceylon and many others, became self-governing, and the Empire of Queen Victoria had shrunk to a much smaller Commonwealth of Nations.

The years since Queen Elizabeth's accession have seen a great change in the lives of ordinary people. High wages have brought to many homes the things which they never had before, such as cars, television sets, refrigerators, and the pleasures of holidays abroad. A National Health Service assures medical attention free of charge to all who are ill, and young people have never had so many opportunities to acquire education and training.

Men orbit the earth and cameras have sent back pictures of the moon. This is the Atomic Age, but science, which has made these things possible, must be controlled if the human race is to continue to enjoy life on this earth.

50   *The rapidly changing world of today.*

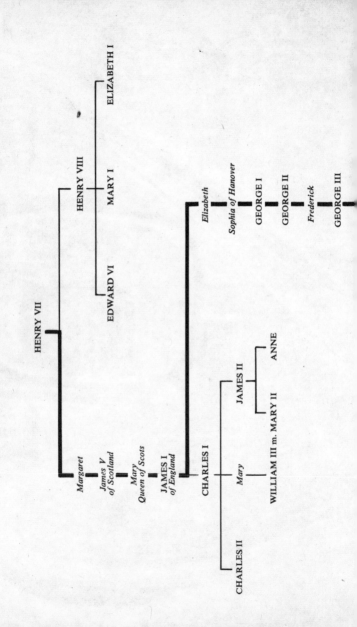

HENRY VII

HENRY VIII

EDWARD VI

MARY I

ELIZABETH I

Margaret

James V
of Scotland

Mary
Queen of Scots

JAMES I
of England

CHARLES I

CHARLES II

Mary

WILLIAM III m. MARY II

JAMES II

ANNE

Elizabeth

Sophia of Hanover

GEORGE I

GEORGE II

Frederick

GEORGE III